Grades 2-3

It's About Time

Chris Nitert

World Teachers Press

Published with the permission of R.I.C. Publications Pty. Ltd.

Copyright © 1997 by Didax, Inc., Rowley, MA 01969. All rights reserved.

First published by R.I.C. Publications Pty. Ltd., Perth, Western Australia.

Printed in the United States of America.

Order Number 2-5030
ISBN 1-885111-43-6

C D E F   99 00

Didax
Educational Resources

395 Main Street
Rowley, MA 01969

INTRODUCTION

The study of time began very early in our history. Time involves more than simply reading clocks. There are many other aspects to time, such as seasons, time zones, measurement of time, timing events, sequencing events and so on. This set of books looks at, and develops understandings and skills with, a wide variety of time-related topics. The activities can be used to teach skills or develop understandings or be used as a support to the teaching program. Objectives for each activity are given to assist in planning the learning program.

Each book develops an understanding of time beyond the simple telling of time from a clock face and includes activities in the following areas:

- calendars
- clocks
- sequencing
- rate
- duration

Integration

Time is an aspect of mathematics that is used in many day-to-day situations and in many different subject areas. Therefore it is a subject that offers numerous opportunities to integrate learning throughout the curriculum. It is important to identify the use of time in these subjects so that students can be aware of the many applications of time in their studies and life in general.

It's About Time will provide you with activities to develop and consolidate these concepts as they arise.

CONTENTS

TEACHER INFORMATION
EXAMPLE LESSON DEVELOPMENT

The following is a lesson development using one of the pages in this book. It is an example of how the activity could be introduced, developed and extended.

INTRODUCTORY WORK

When introducing time as a concept to students it is very important that they are able to relate time to their own lives and their immediate surroundings. It is also important to make students aware that time occurs in different forms (seasonally, annually, hourly etc.). The equipment used to measure time needs to be made readily available to students for study and experimentation. Students need to become familiar and confident when using such equipment in order to develop the concept of time. Opportunity for students to discuss daily, weekly or annual events should be given wherever appropriate.

COMPLETING THE WORKSHEETS

The following is a suggestion for the development and extension of this activity.

1. Discuss when things happen in our day. Talk about when things happen in some type of order.

3. Sequence the events in time order by cutting out the pictures and placing them in the order in which they occur.

2. Discuss usual sequence of events in the day. What do you do first, second and so on.

EXTENSION

The extension of the activity is largely covered by the next activities, however further discussion of time sequence is important. Ask the students to sequence longer periods of time.

WHEN DID IT HAPPEN?

Cut out the pictures below and put them in order from when you woke up. Color the pictures.

World Teachers Press

It's About Time

WHAT DID YOU DO?

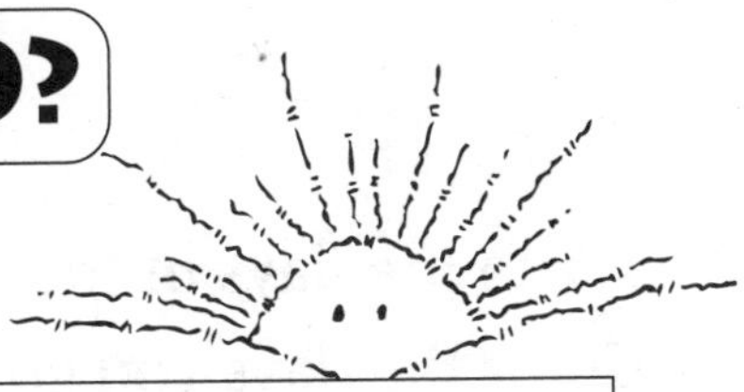

Draw something you do in the morning.
Write what it is.

_____

_____

_____

_____

Draw something you do at lunchtime.
Write what it is.

_____

_____

_____

Draw something you do in the afternoon.
Write what it is.

_____

_____

_____

Draw something you do at night.
Write what it is.

_____

_____

_____

DAYS

Write the days of the week.
Color the days you go to school yellow.
Color the weekend days red.

M

Write the days that come before and after:

_____ **MONDAY** _____

_____ **WEDNESDAY** _____

_____ **SUNDAY** _____

_____ **THURSDAY** _____

_____ **SATURDAY** _____

_____ **TUESDAY** _____

_____ **FRIDAY** _____

WHAT DO YOU DO?

Write and draw what you do on:

Monday morning.

_____

_____

Tuesday afternoon.

_____

_____

Friday after lunch.

_____

_____

Wednesday afternoon.

_____

_____

Thursday after morning recess.

_____

_____

Monday after lunch.

_____

_____

BIRTHDAY TIME

We all have a birthday once a year.
On the chart below fill in your name and the date you have your birthday. Do the same for ten other people.

NAME	DAY	MONTH	YEAR

Complete these birthday dates:

Maternal Grandmother   _____
Maternal Grandfather   _____

Paternal Grandmother   _____
Paternal Grandfather   _____

Mother   _____   Father   _____

Brothers and Sisters _____ _____ _____

BEFORE AND AFTER

Write in the names of the months.
Color this month blue.
Color last month green.
Color next month red.

J		

Write the names of the months that come before and after:

_____ **JUNE** _____

_____ **FEBRUARY** _____

_____ **APRIL** _____

_____ **OCTOBER** _____

_____ **AUGUST** _____

_____ **DECEMBER** _____

_____ **JANUARY** _____

_____ **SEPTEMBER** _____

ONCE A YEAR

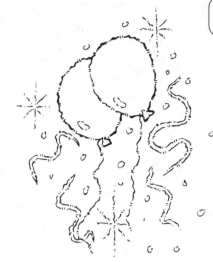

We all have a birthday once a year.

What other things happen only once a year?

_____

_____

_____

On the calendar below circle one person's birthday for each month and write their name below.

JANUARY

S	M	T	W	T	F	S
		1	2	3	4	5
6	7	8	9	10	11	12
13	14	15	16	17	18	19
20	21	22	23	24	25	26
27	28	29	30	31		

FEBRUARY

S	M	T	W	T	F	S
					1	2
3	4	5	6	7	8	9
10	11	12	13	14	15	16
17	18	19	20	21	22	23
24	25	26	27	28		

MARCH

S	M	T	W	T	F	S
31					1	2
3	4	5	6	7	8	9
10	11	12	13	14	15	16
17	18	19	20	21	22	23
24	25	26	27	28	29	30

APRIL

S	M	T	W	T	F	S
	1	2	3	4	5	6
7	8	9	10	11	12	13
14	15	16	17	18	19	20
21	22	23	24	25	26	27
28	29	30				

MAY

S	M	T	W	T	F	S
			1	2	3	4
5	6	7	8	9	10	11
12	13	14	15	16	17	18
19	20	21	22	23	24	25
26	27	28	29	30	31	

JUNE

S	M	T	W	T	F	S
30						1
2	3	4	5	6	7	8
9	10	11	12	13	14	15
16	17	18	19	20	21	22
23	24	25	26	27	28	29

JULY

S	M	T	W	T	F	S
	1	2	3	4	5	6
7	8	9	10	11	12	13
14	15	16	17	18	19	20
21	22	23	24	25	26	27
28	29	30	31			

AUGUST

S	M	T	W	T	F	S
				1	2	3
4	5	6	7	8	9	10
11	12	13	14	15	16	17
18	19	20	21	22	23	24
25	26	27	28	29	30	31

SEPTEMBER

S	M	T	W	T	F	S
1	2	3	4	5	6	7
8	9	10	11	12	13	14
15	16	17	18	19	20	21
22	23	24	25	26	27	28
29	30					

OCTOBER

S	M	T	W	T	F	S
		1	2	3	4	5
6	7	8	9	10	11	12
13	14	15	16	17	18	19
20	21	22	23	24	25	26
27	28	29	30	31		

NOVEMBER

S	M	T	W	T	F	S
					1	2
3	4	5	6	7	8	9
10	11	12	13	14	15	16
17	18	19	20	21	22	23
24	25	26	27	28	29	30

DECEMBER

S	M	T	W	T	F	S
1	2	3	4	5	6	7
8	9	10	11	12	13	14
15	16	17	18	19	20	21
22	23	24	25	26	27	28
29	30	31				

_____ _____ _____ _____

Can you think of any special events that happen in:

December? _____

January? _____

April? _____

July? _____

September? _____

MONTHS AND SEASONS

**Cut out the months at the bottom of the page
and glue them into the correct season.**

SUMMER	AUTUMN
WINTER	**SPRING**

JANUARY	FEBRUARY	MARCH
APRIL	MAY	JUNE
JULY	AUGUST	SEPTEMBER
OCTOBER	NOVEMBER	DECEMBER

MAKE A CLOCK

Cut and glue the numbers onto the clock.

Make sure they are in their correct places.

Cut out the hands and use a pin to make the clock.

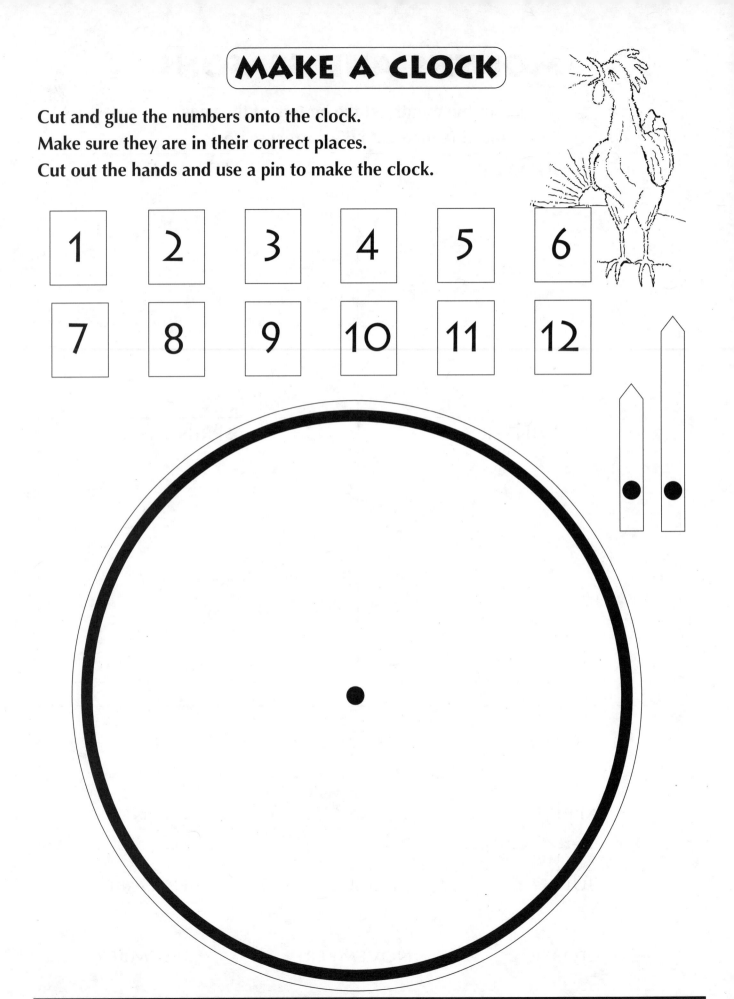

World Teachers Press

It's About Time

MISSING NUMBERS

Write in the missing numbers on the clock faces.

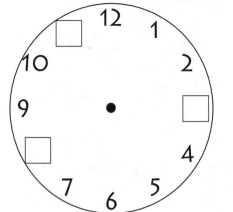

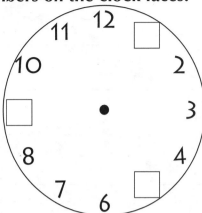

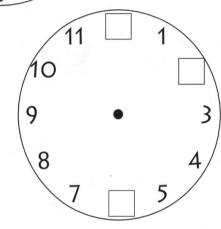

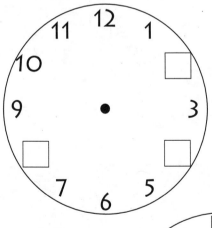

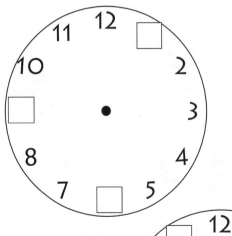

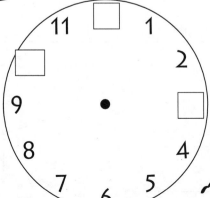

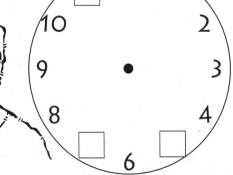

READING TIME

Read the times on the clock faces and write about something you do at that time.

_____

_____

_____

_____

_____

_____

_____

_____

_____

_____

_____

_____

_____

_____

_____

_____

_____

World Teachers Press

It's About Time

CALENDAR STUDY

Answer the questions about the calendar for the months of April and May.

APRIL

SUN	MON	TUES	WED	THU	FRI	SAT
1	2	3	4	5	6	7
8	9	10	11	12	13	14
15	16	17	18	19	20	21
22	23	24	25	26	27	28
29	30					

1. What is the first day of April?

   _____

2. What is the last day of April?

   _____

3. How many Tuesdays are there in

   April? _____

4. What is the date of the third Friday of April?

   _____

5. What is the date of the second

   Wednesday? _____

6. What would be the last day of

   March? _____

7. What is the first day of May?

   _____

8. What is the last day of May?

   _____

9. How many Mondays are there in

   May? _____

10. What is the date of the third

    Thursday of May? _____

11. What is the date of the second

    Wednesday? _____

12. What would be the first day of

    June? _____

MAY

SUN	MON	TUES	WED	THU	FRI	SAT
		1	2	3	4	5
6	7	8	9	10	11	12
13	14	15	16	17	18	19
20	21	22	23	24	25	26
27	28	29	30	31		

LAST WEEK

Write or draw about something that happened or that you did on these days last week. On the clock face near the day, draw in the time this happened.

SUNDAY	
MONDAY	
TUESDAY	
WEDNESDAY	
THURSDAY	
FRIDAY	
SATURDAY	

World Teachers Press

It's About Time

HOW LONG?

How long do you think it would take you to:

- write your name? _____

- say the alphabet?

- put a cross in every one of the boxes in the 100 chart?

1	2	3	4	5	6	7	8	9	10
11	12	13	14	15	16	17	18	19	20
21	22	23	24	25	26	27	28	29	30
31	32	33	34	35	36	37	38	39	40
41	42	43	44	45	46	47	48	49	50
51	52	53	54	55	56	57	58	59	60
61	62	63	64	65	66	67	68	69	70
71	72	73	74	75	76	77	78	79	80
81	82	83	84	85	86	87	88	89	90
91	92	93	94	95	96	97	98	99	100

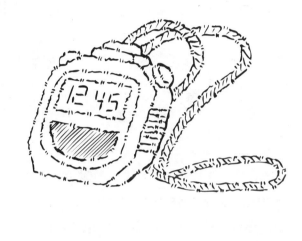

- write down the months of the year?

_____

_____

- color this pattern neatly?

FIND YOUR WAY

Find your way around the numbers 1 to 20.

Have someone time you.

Repeat this three times and write down how long each try took.

First try ☐

Second try ☐

Third try ☐

9 7 1
14 16
19 10
3 5
12 20
11 6
2 17
8 15 18 4 13

Find each letter of the alphabet.

Have someone time you.

Repeat this three times and write down how long each try took.

First try ☐

Second try ☐

Third try ☐

C L F
U
V H N
E
Z W
J B
D S O R
T
X I Q
G K
P A
Y M

TWO CLOCKS

There are two types of clocks or watches:

- a clock with a face and hands
- a clock with just numbers (a digital clock).

= 6 o'clock   **6:00** = 6 o'clock

A clock with a face and hands   **A digital clock**

Write the digital times for these clock faces.

1.

2.

3.

4.

5.

6.

Draw in the clock hands for these digital times.

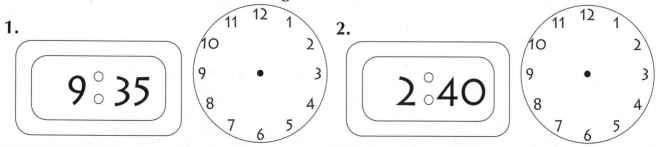

1.   **9:35**

2.   **2:40**

WHAT TIME IS IT WHEN . . . ?

Draw in the times to answer the questions below.

What time is it when:

1. you wake up in the morning?

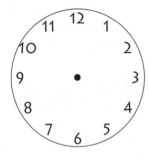

2. you go to school?

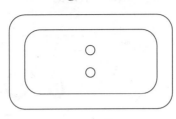

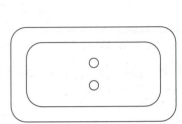

3. you eat lunch?

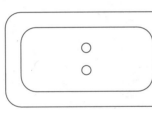

4. you go home?

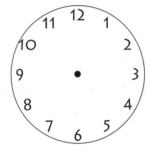

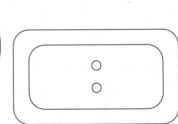

5. you eat dinner?

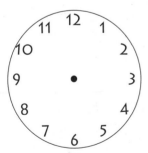

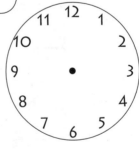

6. you go to bed?

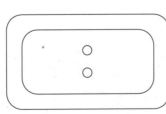

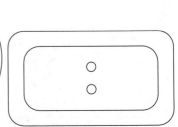

TIME WORDS

Use your dictionary to help you explain the meaning of these words and phrases.

1. Next week _____

2. Midnight _____

3. The day after tomorrow _____

4. Noon _____

5. Weekly _____

6. Daily _____

7. Fortnight _____

8. Midday _____

Select the correct word in these sentences.

1. I ate my lunch at 12 (*noon/midnight*) on Wednesday.

2. My pet rabbit is being shown at the fair (*last/next*) week.

3. The dentist brushes her teeth twice (*weekly/daily*).

4. The day after (*yesterday/tomorrow*), dad is going overseas for work.

5. Mother washes the clothes (*fortnightly/weekly*) on Tuesdays.

6. I love bread that is baked fresh (*weekly/daily*).

7. My brother loves to swim (*yearly/weekly*) to keep fit.

8. People who work, get paid (*weekly/yearly*).

9. You must remember to visit the dentist (*yearly/weekly*).

10. New babies need to be fed (*daily/hourly*) to be healthy.

TIME SEARCH

How many of the time words below can you find in the word search?
Words can be found going across and down.

W	E	D	N	E	S	D	A	Y	M	O	N	T	H	A	T
S	P	R	I	N	G	B	N	I	G	H	T	S	C	Y	U
A	D	S	T	H	U	R	S	D	A	Y	M	U	Y	E	E
F	E	A	M	I	D	N	I	G	H	T	I	M	E	A	S
T	F	T	W	G	M	I	N	U	T	E	D	M	S	R	D
E	W	U	E	H	I	T	O	D	A	Y	D	E	T	J	A
R	I	R	E	S	E	C	O	N	D	K	A	R	E	D	Y
N	N	D	K	M	O	R	N	I	N	G	Y	L	R	I	S
O	T	A	F	O	R	T	N	I	G	H	T	M	D	G	U
O	E	Y	T	I	M	E	F	R	I	D	A	Y	A	I	N
N	R	N	A	U	T	U	M	N	H	O	U	R	Y	T	D
D	A	Y	O	T	O	M	O	R	R	O	W	P	Q	A	A
R	C	L	O	C	K	S	T	M	O	N	D	A	Y	L	Y

HOUR	MINUTE	SECOND
AFTERNOON	MORNING	NIGHT
MIDDAY	MIDNIGHT	TOMORROW
TODAY	YESTERDAY	DAY
WEEK	FORTNIGHT	MONTH
YEAR	TIME	DIGITAL
CLOCK	MONDAY	TUESDAY
WEDNESDAY	THURSDAY	FRIDAY
SATURDAY	SUNDAY	WINTER
SUMMER	AUTUMN	SPRING

COUNTING BY FIVES

Count by fives to 60.

5					

					60

Use this information to help you read the time on the clock faces below, to the nearest five minutes.

_____      _____

   _____      _____

_____      _____

   _____      _____

_____      _____

IF THE TIME IS . . .

If the time is 12 noon, how much time has gone by since:

9:00 a.m.? _____

5:00 a.m.? _____

1:00 a.m.? _____

10:30 a.m.? _____

11:05 a.m.? _____

6:45 a.m.? _____

7:25 a.m.? _____

8:40 a.m.? _____

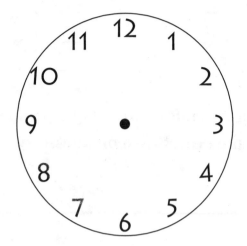

If the time is 12 noon, how long will it take before it is:

3:00 p.m.? _____

6:00 p.m.? _____

10:00 p.m.? _____

11:30 p.m.? _____

2:35 p.m.? _____

9:45 p.m.? _____

1:55 p.m.? _____

How much time is there between:

4:00 a.m. and 11:00 a.m.? _____

6:00 p.m. and 5:00 a.m.? _____

10:00 a.m. and 7:00 p.m.? _____

9:00 p.m. and 3:30 a.m. ?_____

12:30 a.m. and 11:30 p.m.? _____

Complete this grid.

TIME STARTED	TIME FINISHED	TIME TAKEN
8:00 p.m.		2 hours
7:00 a.m.	1:00 p.m.	
	3:15 p.m.	3 hours
9:15 p.m.	12:30 p.m.	
	4:05 p.m.	3 hours 15 minutes

 World Teachers Press *It's About Time*

MONTHS

Unscramble the month words below.

LPARI _____ HMARC _____

RYFBRAUE _____ BOREOTC _____

NYJAARU _____ AMY _____

RTEBESEMP _____ ENUJ _____

ORENBVME _____ UTSGAU _____

MECREBDE _____ LYJU _____

Write the months of the year in alphabetical order.

_____ _____ _____

_____ _____ _____

_____ _____ _____

_____ _____ _____

What is the:

1. first month of the year? _____

2. fourth month of the year? _____

3. tenth month of the year? _____

4. sixth month of the year? _____

5. seventh month of the year? _____

6. last month of the year? _____

7. sixth day of the week? _____

8. second day of the week? _____

9. fourth day of the week? _____

10. first day of the week? _____

TIME CROSSWORD PUZZLE

Can you complete the crossword puzzle below?
All the answers are either days of the week or months of the year.

ACROSS

4. The last day of the working week.
5. The first day of the working week.
6. The last day of the weekend.
7. The month before August.
8. The last month of the year.
10. A three-letter month.
11. The tenth month of the year.

DOWN

1. The month after May.
2. The first day of the weekend.
3. The month before February.
9. The third month of the year.

1. Sally left for school at 8:35 a.m.
   She arrived at school at 8:50 a.m.
   How many minutes did she take to walk to school? _____

2. A TV program started at 5:15 p.m. The program finished at 5:45 p.m. For how long did the TV program last? _____

3. Ian started his homework at 4:25 p.m.
   He finished his homework at 5:05 p.m.
   How much time did Ian spend on his homework? _____

4. The lesson started when the classroom clock looked like this.

   The lesson finished when the classroom clock looked like this.

   How long did the lesson last? _____

5. The ball game started at 10:30 a.m.
   The game finished at 1:05 p.m.
   How many hours and minutes did the game last? _____
   Draw the starting and finishing times on the clocks below.

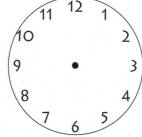

6. Andy went to football practice at 4:30 p.m.
   He came home at 5:45 p.m.
   How long was Andy away at football practice? _____

ONE MINUTE

How much of this pattern can you color (using three colors only) in one minute?

Using cubes, how many of these shapes can you build in one minute?

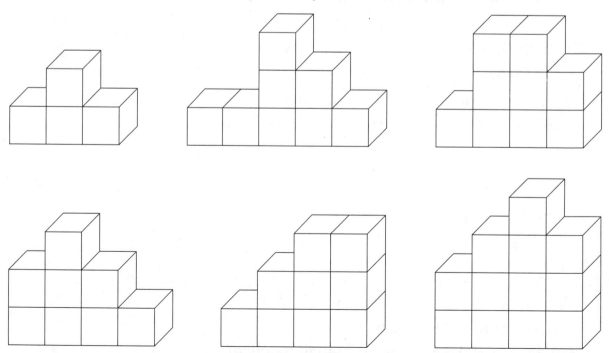

TIMES GRAPH

The graph below shows the different times (in seconds) it took seven students to say the five times table.

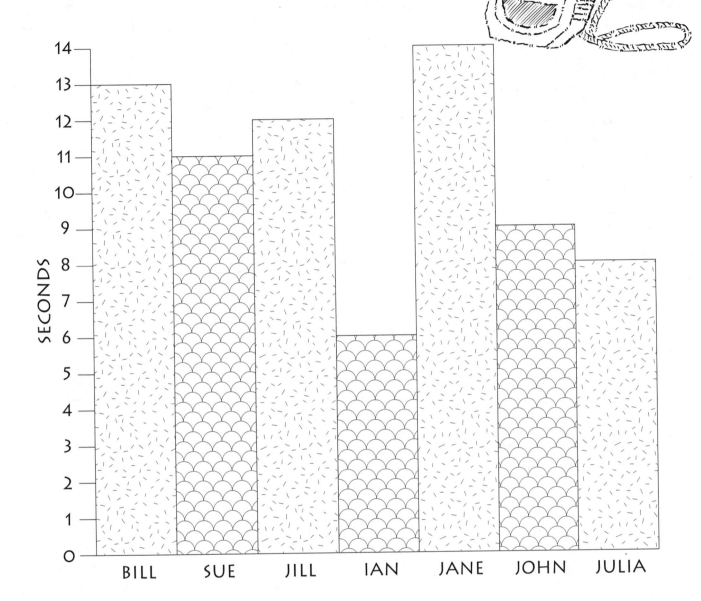

1. Put the students in order from fastest to slowest in saying the five times table.

   _____

2. What was the difference in time between the quickest and slowest student?

   _____

3. Time yourself and three of your friends to see who you can beat from the students in the graph.

12-HOUR DIARY

Keep an hourly diary for the twelve hours between
6 o'clock in the morning and 6 o'clock in the evening.
Write about what you were doing at that time.

6:00 a.m. _____

7:00 a.m. _____

8:00 a.m. _____

9:00 a.m. _____

10:00 a.m. _____

11:00 a.m. _____

12:00 a.m. _____

1:00 p.m. _____

2:00 p.m. _____

3:00 p.m. _____

4:00 p.m. _____

5:00 p.m. _____

6:00 p.m. _____

What do you do for the rest of the day?

_____

_____

_____

World Teachers Press

It's About Time

HOW LONG DOES IT TAKE?

On the left are things that happen. On the right there are times.
Draw a line to match the happenings with their correct times.

To run 100 yards •	• 1 minute
Age to start school •	• 1 to 1.5 hours
To run one mile •	• 6 to 7 hours
For an apple to grow •	• 40 to 50 minutes
To count to 100 •	• 11 to 12 years
Spend a day at school •	• 100 to 200 days
To walk three miles •	• 10 to 20 seconds
To play a tape or CD •	• 4 to 6 minutes
To reach high school age •	• 4 to 5 years

Use your dictionary to help you find the meaning of these time words.

Century _____

_____

Annual _____

_____

Decade _____

_____

Metronome _____

_____

Biannual _____

_____

FIND THE DAYS

On the calendar, shade the dates listed below.
Next to each date write in the day of the week on which it falls.

1. Christmas Day (Dec. 25) _____

2. St. Patrick's Day (March 17) _____

3. MLK's birthday (Jan. 15) _____

4. New Year's Day (Jan. 1) _____

5. Independence Day (July 4) _____

6. Election Day (Nov. 5) _____

7. Your birthday _____

8. Your mother's birthday _____

9. Your father's birthday _____

10. A friend's birthday _____

11. Your teacher's birthday _____

12. Valentine's Day (Feb. 14) _____

13. Mother's Day _____

14. Father's Day _____

15. Halloween (Oct. 31) _____

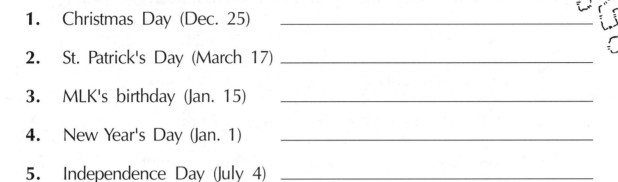

JANUARY

S	M	T	W	T	F	S
		1	2	3	4	5
6	7	8	9	10	11	12
13	14	15	16	17	18	19
20	21	22	23	24	25	26
27	28	29	30	31		

FEBRUARY

S	M	T	W	T	F	S
					1	2
3	4	5	6	7	8	9
10	11	12	13	14	15	16
17	18	19	20	21	22	23
24	25	26	27	28		

MARCH

S	M	T	W	T	F	S
31					1	2
3	4	5	6	7	8	9
10	11	12	13	14	15	16
17	18	19	20	21	22	23
24	25	26	27	28	29	30

APRIL

S	M	T	W	T	F	S
	1	2	3	4	5	6
7	8	9	10	11	12	13
14	15	16	17	18	19	20
21	22	23	24	25	26	27
28	29	30				

MAY

S	M	T	W	T	F	S
			1	2	3	4
5	6	7	8	9	10	11
12	13	14	15	16	17	18
19	20	21	22	23	24	25
26	27	28	29	30	31	

JUNE

S	M	T	W	T	F	S
30						1
2	3	4	5	6	7	8
9	10	11	12	13	14	15
16	17	18	19	20	21	22
23	24	25	26	27	28	29

JULY

S	M	T	W	T	F	S
	1	2	3	4	5	6
7	8	9	10	11	12	13
14	15	16	17	18	19	20
21	22	23	24	25	26	27
28	29	30	31			

AUGUST

S	M	T	W	T	F	S
				1	2	3
4	5	6	7	8	9	10
11	12	13	14	15	16	17
18	19	20	21	22	23	24
25	26	27	28	29	30	31

SEPTEMBER

S	M	T	W	T	F	S
1	2	3	4	5	6	7
8	9	10	11	12	13	14
15	16	17	18	19	20	21
22	23	24	25	26	27	28
29	30					

OCTOBER

S	M	T	W	T	F	S
		1	2	3	4	5
6	7	8	9	10	11	12
13	14	15	16	17	18	19
20	21	22	23	24	25	26
27	28	29	30	31		

NOVEMBER

S	M	T	W	T	F	S
					1	2
3	4	5	6	7	8	9
10	11	12	13	14	15	16
17	18	19	20	21	22	23
24	25	26	27	28	29	30

DECEMBER

S	M	T	W	T	F	S
1	2	3	4	5	6	7
8	9	10	11	12	13	14
15	16	17	18	19	20	21
22	23	24	25	26	27	28
29	30	31				

World Teachers Press

It's About Time

DAY AND DATE

Use the calendar to answer the questions below.
What is the day and date:

1. five days after June 3   _____ _____

2. one week after April 5   _____ _____

3. one week before February 2   _____ _____

4. two weeks after May 25   _____ _____

5. eight days before December 7   _____ _____

6. three weeks after Halloween   _____ _____

7. a week after November 28   _____ _____

8. two Fridays after March 6   _____ _____

9. 12 days before Christmas   _____ _____

10. 16 days before your birthday   _____ _____

11. the Monday before May 9   _____ _____

12. three weeks after January 7   _____ _____

13. four days before May 21   _____ _____

14. six weeks before November 14   _____ _____

15. 40 days after New Year's Day   _____ _____

JANUARY
S	M	T	W	T	F	S
		1	2	3	4	5
6	7	8	9	10	11	12
13	14	15	16	17	18	19
20	21	22	23	24	25	26
27	28	29	30	31		

FEBRUARY
S	M	T	W	T	F	S
					1	2
3	4	5	6	7	8	9
10	11	12	13	14	15	16
17	18	19	20	21	22	23
24	25	26	27	28		

MARCH
S	M	T	W	T	F	S
31					1	2
3	4	5	6	7	8	9
10	11	12	13	14	15	16
17	18	19	20	21	22	23
24	25	26	27	28	29	30

APRIL
S	M	T	W	T	F	S
	1	2	3	4	5	6
7	8	9	10	11	12	13
14	15	16	17	18	19	20
21	22	23	24	25	26	27
28	29	30				

MAY
S	M	T	W	T	F	S
			1	2	3	4
5	6	7	8	9	10	11
12	13	14	15	16	17	18
19	20	21	22	23	24	25
26	27	28	29	30	31	

JUNE
S	M	T	W	T	F	S
30						1
2	3	4	5	6	7	8
9	10	11	12	13	14	15
16	17	18	19	20	21	22
23	24	25	26	27	28	29

JULY
S	M	T	W	T	F	S
	1	2	3	4	5	6
7	8	9	10	11	12	13
14	15	16	17	18	19	20
21	22	23	24	25	26	27
28	29	30	31			

AUGUST
S	M	T	W	T	F	S
				1	2	3
4	5	6	7	8	9	10
11	12	13	14	15	16	17
18	19	20	21	22	23	24
25	26	27	28	29	30	31

SEPTEMBER
S	M	T	W	T	F	S
1	2	3	4	5	6	7
8	9	10	11	12	13	14
15	16	17	18	19	20	21
22	23	24	25	26	27	28
29	30					

OCTOBER
S	M	T	W	T	F	S
		1	2	3	4	5
6	7	8	9	10	11	12
13	14	15	16	17	18	19
20	21	22	23	24	25	26
27	28	29	30	31		

NOVEMBER
S	M	T	W	T	F	S
					1	2
3	4	5	6	7	8	9
10	11	12	13	14	15	16
17	18	19	20	21	22	23
24	25	26	27	28	29	30

DECEMBER
S	M	T	W	T	F	S
1	2	3	4	5	6	7
8	9	10	11	12	13	14
15	16	17	18	19	20	21
22	23	24	25	26	27	28
29	30	31				

HOW MANY?

Use the calendar to answer the questions below.
How many:

1. Fridays in January _____

2. Mondays in May _____

3. Thursdays in December _____

4. Sundays in June _____

5. Fridays fall on the 2nd of a month _____

6. months begin on a Sunday _____

7. months end on a Friday _____

8. Tuesdays fall on the 21st of a month _____

9. Mondays are there in the year _____

10. Fridays are there in the year _____

11. Sundays are there in the year _____

12. Wednesdays are there in the year _____

13. months begin on a Monday _____

14. Thursdays in February _____

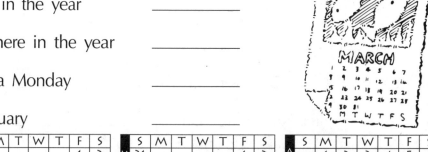

JANUARY	S	M	T	W	T	F	S
			1	2	3	4	5
	6	7	8	9	10	11	12
	13	14	15	16	17	18	19
	20	21	22	23	24	25	26
	27	28	29	30	31		

FEBRUARY	S	M	T	W	T	F	S
						1	2
	3	4	5	6	7	8	9
	10	11	12	13	14	15	16
	17	18	19	20	21	22	23
	24	25	26	27	28		

MARCH	S	M	T	W	T	F	S
	31					1	2
	3	4	5	6	7	8	9
	10	11	12	13	14	15	16
	17	18	19	20	21	22	23
	24	25	26	27	28	29	30

APRIL	S	M	T	W	T	F	S
		1	2	3	4	5	6
	7	8	9	10	11	12	13
	14	15	16	17	18	19	20
	21	22	23	24	25	26	27
	28	29	30				

MAY	S	M	T	W	T	F	S
				1	2	3	4
	5	6	7	8	9	10	11
	12	13	14	15	16	17	18
	19	20	21	22	23	24	25
	26	27	28	29	30	31	

JUNE	S	M	T	W	T	F	S
	30						1
	2	3	4	5	6	7	8
	9	10	11	12	13	14	15
	16	17	18	19	20	21	22
	23	24	25	26	27	28	29

JULY	S	M	T	W	T	F	S
		1	2	3	4	5	6
	7	8	9	10	11	12	13
	14	15	16	17	18	19	20
	21	22	23	24	25	26	27
	28	29	30	31			

AUGUST	S	M	T	W	T	F	S
					1	2	3
	4	5	6	7	8	9	10
	11	12	13	14	15	16	17
	18	19	20	21	22	23	24
	25	26	27	28	29	30	31

SEPTEMBER	S	M	T	W	T	F	S
	1	2	3	4	5	6	7
	8	9	10	11	12	13	14
	15	16	17	18	19	20	21
	22	23	24	25	26	27	28
	29	30					

OCTOBER	S	M	T	W	T	F	S
			1	2	3	4	5
	6	7	8	9	10	11	12
	13	14	15	16	17	18	19
	20	21	22	23	24	25	26
	27	28	29	30	31		

NOVEMBER	S	M	T	W	T	F	S
						1	2
	3	4	5	6	7	8	9
	10	11	12	13	14	15	16
	17	18	19	20	21	22	23
	24	25	26	27	28	29	30

DECEMBER	S	M	T	W	T	F	S
	1	2	3	4	5	6	7
	8	9	10	11	12	13	14
	15	16	17	18	19	20	21
	22	23	24	25	26	27	28
	29	30	31				

World Teachers Press

It's About Time

SCHOOL BIRTHDAYS

Below is a bar graph that shows the number of students' birthdays in each month at East Hill School.
Study the graph and answer the questions.

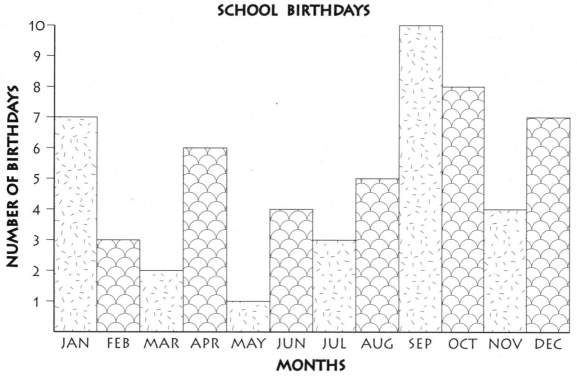

SCHOOL BIRTHDAYS

1. In which month do the most number of birthdays fall? _____

2. In which month do the least number of birthdays fall? _____

3. What is the difference in the number of birthdays between the above two months? _____

4. Two pairs of months have the same number of birthdays. Name them.

   _____ and _____ , _____ and _____ .

5. How many students attend East Hill School? _____

6. What is the difference between the number of birthdays which fall in November and March? _____

7. In which month are there eight birthdays? _____

8. Which months could add together to give 10 birthday people?

   _____   _____

CLASS BIRTHDAYS

Survey your class to find out how many birthdays there are in each month of the year. Then graph your results and answer the questions.

MONTH	TALLY	MONTH	TALLY
JANUARY		JULY	
FEBRUARY		AUGUST	
MARCH		SEPTEMBER	
APRIL		OCTOBER	
MAY		NOVEMBER	
JUNE		DECEMBER	

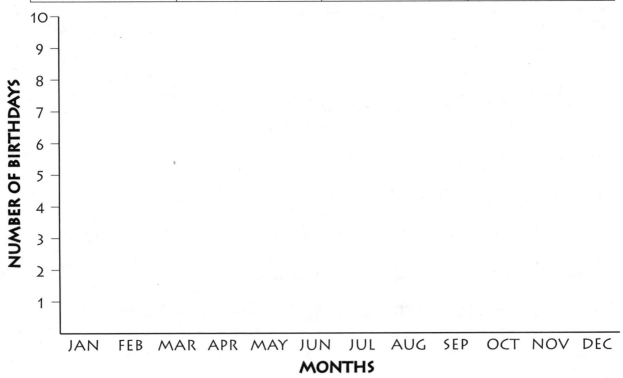

1. Which month has the most number of birthdays? _____

2. Which month has the least number of birthdays? _____

3. Do another survey, but use dates rather than months.

4. What do you find when using dates rather than months? _____

_____

World Teachers Press
It's About Time

MEASURING TIME

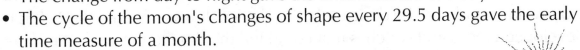

Humans have measured time since the earliest days. Time measuring was and still is based on change.

- The change from day to night gave the time measure of a day.
- The cycle of the moon's changes of shape every 29.5 days gave the early time measure of a month.
- The change in seasons gave the time measure of a year.

Use your dictionary and an encyclopedia to help you explain what causes:

DAY AND NIGHT

_____

_____

_____

_____

A LUNAR MONTH

_____

_____

_____

_____

A YEAR

_____

_____

_____

_____

TIME DEVICES

As humans became more civilized, the measuring of time needed to become more accurate. The first devices, such as the sundial, could measure time to the nearest hour. However, this could only be done during a sunny day. Measuring time at night and on cloudy days could not be done using this device. It was not until the 1700s that humans developed clocks and watches that could tell the time to the nearest minute. It was not until recently that electronic and atomic clocks have allowed humans to tell the time to the nearest 1,000th of a second.

Use your dictionary and an encyclopedia to explain how the time devices below work.

1. *SUNDIAL* _____

_____

_____

_____

2. *HOURGLASS* _____

_____

_____

_____

3. *WATER CLOCK* _____

_____

_____

_____

4. *DIGITAL CLOCK* _____

_____

_____

_____

TIME ZONES

Clocks all around the world show different times, depending upon their location. If all clocks showed the same time, for example 12:00, then somewhere in the world people would be watching the sunrise or sunset or eating dinner. As soon as one place is east or west of another place the sun is in a different position and, therefore, it is a different time. To stop confusion about what time of the day it is from one part of the world to another, time zones have been set up.

Use this information, an atlas and the map on this page to answer the questions below.

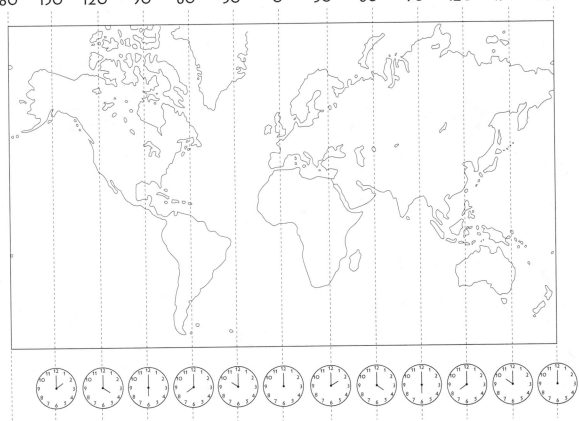

1. How many time zones are in the continent of Africa? _____

2. Which continent has only two time zones? _____

3. North America has four time zones?   True   False

4. How many time zones are in the continent of Europe? _____

5. The continent of Asia has five time zones?   True   False

6. Which continent has the most number of time zones? _____

7. Which continent has the least number of time zones? _____

8. Australia has three time zones?   True   False

About the Author

Chris Nitert, Perth, Western Australia.
Chris has over 15 years experience in Australian primary schools as a classroom teacher, schools advisory teacher and administrator. This title and others authored by Chris are a product of this experience and a wish to present ideas to teachers in an easy-to-understand and practice format.